Be a Friend to Trees

Description

Learners explore the phenomenon that many things they use every day come from trees. They learn the importance of trees as sources of food, shelter, and oxygen for people and animals, and ways to conserve trees.

Alignment With the *Next Generation Science Standards*

Performance Expectations

K-ESS3-1: Use a model to represent the relationship between the needs of different plants and animals (including humans) and the places they live.

K-ESS3-3: Communicate solutions that will reduce the impact of humans on the land, water, air, and/or other living things in the local environment.

Science and Engineering Practices	Disciplinary Core Ideas	Crosscutting Concepts
Obtaining, Evaluating, and Communicating Information Read grade-appropriate texts and/ or use media to obtain scientific and/or technical information to determine patterns in and/or evidence about the natural and designed world(s). Communicate information or design ideas and/or solutions with others in oral and/or written forms using models, drawings, writing, or numbers that provide detail about scientific ideas, practices, and/or design ideas.	ESS3.A: Natural Resources Living things need water, air, and resources from the land, and they live in places that have the things they need. Humans use natural resources for everything they do. ESS3.C: Human Impacts on Earth Systems Things that people do to live comfortably can affect the world around them. But they can make choices that reduce their impacts on the land, water, air, and other living things.	Cause and Effect Events have causes that generate observable patterns. Systems and System Models Systems in the natural and designed world have parts that work together.

Note: The activities in this lesson will help students move toward the performance expectations listed, which is the goal after multiple activities. However, the activities will not by themselves be sufficient to reach the performance expectations.

Featured Picture Books

TITLE: **Our Tree Named Steve**
AUTHOR: **Alan Zweibel**
ILLUSTRATOR: **David Catrow**
PUBLISHER: **G. P. Putnam's Sons**
YEAR: **2005**
GENRE: **Story**
SUMMARY: *In a letter to his children that is both humorous and poignant, a father recounts memories of the role that Steve, the tree in their front yard, has played in their lives.*

TITLE: **Be a Friend to Trees**
AUTHOR: **Patricia Lauber**
ILLUSTRATOR: **Holly Keller**
PUBLISHER: **HarperTrophy**
YEAR: **1994**
GENRE: **Non-Narrative Information**
SUMMARY: *This book discusses the importance of trees as sources of food, oxygen, and other essential things, and gives helpful tips for conserving this important natural resource.*

Time Needed

This lesson will take several class periods. Suggested scheduling is as follows:

Session 1: Engage with Our Tree Named Steve Read-Aloud

Session 2: Explore with Sorting Chart and Explain with Be a Friend to Trees Read-Aloud

Session 3: Elaborate with My Favorite Tree

Session 4: Evaluate with We Need Trees Poster and Be a Friend to Trees Picture

Materials

For Sorting Chart (per group of 3–5 students; this activity can also be done as a class, which would require just one set of materials.)

- Sorting chart made from chart paper with a large Venn diagram drawn on it
- Boxes or bins, 1 per group, filled with several of the following items that came from trees and items that did not come from trees (either the actual objects or pictures of the objects) described in the book Be a Friend to Trees

National Science Teaching Association

From Trees:

- Wooden block
- Writing or construction paper
- Newspaper
- Small cardboard box or paper milk carton
- Apple, orange, pear, cherry, or peach
- Walnut, almond, pecan, or hazelnut in the shell (Check to see if you have students with tree nut allergies in your class, and use only pictures if you do.)
- Small tree branch with leaves
- Pine needles
- Piece of tree bark
- Paper towel
- Paper grocery bag
- Sealed baggie or balloon blown up with air and marked "Oxygen" (This will represent oxygen although it also contains other gases.)

SAFETY

- If any students have tree nut allergies, use pictures instead of actual tree nuts.
- Use caution when working with scissors to avoid cutting or puncturing skin or eyes.

Not From Trees:

- Plastic objects (such as small toys, markers, balls, and containers)
- Metal objects (such as keys, foil, and spoons)
- Glass marble
- Rock
- Small pumpkin, squash, carrot, or potato
- Cotton, polyester, or nylon cloth
- Reusable net or canvas grocery bag
- Sealed baggie blown up with air and marked "Carbon Dioxide" (This will represent carbon dioxide although it contains other gases.)

From Both:

- Pencil with eraser
- Plastic bottle of maple syrup
- Chocolate in a foil wrapper

For My Favorite Tree (per student)

- Crayon with the paper removed
- Pencil
- Clipboard (or notebook to use as a writing surface)

For We Need Trees Poster

- Leaf cutouts on green paper
- Scissors

For Be a Friend to Trees Picture

- Drawing paper
- Drawing supplies

Student Pages

- My Favorite Tree Journal (4 single-sided pages stapled together)
- Leaf Cutout (copied on green paper)
- STEM Everywhere

Background for Teachers

Humans depend on Earth for many different natural resources, including air, water, soil, energy, animals, and plants. Some of these resources are renewable over human lifetimes, and some are nonrenewable (such as mineral resources and fossil fuels). Trees are one of Earth's most valuable natural resources. We depend on trees for food and wood products, water and soil conservation, shade, beauty, and, most important, the oxygen they add to the air. In addition, trees remove carbon dioxide from the atmosphere by storing carbon in leaves, branches, and primarily in the trunk as wood.

Although trees are a renewable resource that can be planted, grown, and harvested for timber, there are limits to the renewability of this resource. It is essential for students to understand and appreciate the importance of trees to humans and all life on Earth, and to realize that their actions can have an impact on trees. In this lesson, students explore our dependence on trees by observing and sorting various products that come from them. After reading about how humans and other animals depend on trees, they also learn a variety of ways that they can "be a friend to trees" by conserving and replacing them. Nurturing a sense of wonder about trees will encourage students to do more to protect this vital resource.

Learning Progressions

Below are the DCI grade band endpoints for grades K–2 and 3–5. These are provided to show how student understanding of the DCIs in this lesson will progress in future grade levels.

DCIs	Grades K–2	Grades 3–5
ESS3.A: Natural Resources	• Living things need water, air, and resources from the land, and they live in places that have the things they need. Humans use natural resources for everything they do.	• Energy and fuels that humans use are derived from natural sources, and their use affects the environment in multiple ways. Some resources are renewable over time, and others are not.
ESS3.C: Human Impacts on Earth Systems	• Things that people do to live comfortably can affect the world around them. But they can make choices that reduce their impacts on the land, water, air, and other living things.	• Human activities in agriculture, industry, and everyday life have had major effects on the land, vegetation, streams, ocean, air, and even outer space. But individuals and communities are doing things to help protect Earth's resources and environments.

Source: Willard, T., ed. 2015. The NSTA quick-reference guide to the NGSS: Elementary school. Arlington, VA: NSTA Press.

engage

Our Tree Named Steve **Read-Aloud**

Connecting to the Common Core
Reading: Literature
KEY IDEAS AND DETAILS: K.1

Turn and Talk

Before reading the book Our Tree Named Steve, engage students by saying, "From where you are sitting, look around and think of everything in this room that might be different if there were no such thing as a tree." Allow some quiet thinking time, and then have students turn and talk to a neighbor.

Inferring

Explain that you have a book to share about a very special tree. Show the cover of Our Tree Named Steve, and then introduce the author and illustrator. Ask

? What are you thinking this story is about? Why do you think so?

Synthesizing

Read the book aloud, stopping after page 5 ("… Mom and I got the hint and asked the builder to please save Steve.") Then ask

? Now what are you thinking this story is about?

You may want to stop at key points in the story to allow students to discuss their thinking about the story's meaning.

Monitoring Comprehension

After reading the last page that shows the tree house, pause to model how good readers monitor their comprehension by verbalizing your "inner conver-

sation." You might say, "I wonder what the author means by this? Oh, I see the tree house. They built a tree house out of Steve."

Questioning

After reading, create a graphic organizer by drawing a large tree trunk on the board or chart paper and labeling it "Steve." Ask

? How did the tree get its name? (The youngest daughter couldn't pronounce the word tree and called it "Steve.")

You can write the students' responses to the following two questions as "branches" of the tree. Ask

? How did the family use this special tree when it was alive? (Answers can include the following: as a swing holder, target, third base, hiding place, jump-rope turner, clothesline, hammock-holder, and sewer-water remover.)

OUR TREE NAMED STEVE *GRAPHIC ORGANIZER*

SORTING OBJECTS

? How did the family use the tree after it blew over in the storm? (They used the wood to build a tree house.)

Then, ask

? How did the tree protect the family "to the very end"? (It didn't fall on their house, the swings, the dog's house, or the garden.)

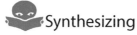 Synthesizing

Ask

? Now what are you thinking the story is about?

? How does the story make you feel?

? Have you ever had a special tree? What made it special?

? What are some ways that trees help us?

explore

Sorting Chart

In advance, prepare boxes or bins filled with an assortment of items that came from trees, items that did not come from trees, and items that contain both wood products and other materials (see "Materials" list). Explain that students will be learning about some of the ways that trees help us by doing a sorting activity and then reading a nonfiction book. Divide students into groups, and distribute to each group a bin and a Sorting Chart made from chart paper with a Venn diagram (two large intersecting circles) drawn on it. Have students label one circle "From Trees," the other circle "Not From Trees," and the intersection of the circles "Both."

Then have groups observe each object carefully, discuss whether or not they think it came from trees and why, and place it in the appropriate cir-

cle on the chart. If they are not sure about how an object should be grouped, they can leave it in the bin for now.

Invite students to justify how they sorted the objects. Ask

? What are some of the objects you think came from trees? Why do you think so?

? What are some of the objects you think did not come from trees? Why do you think so?

? Were there any objects you were unsure about? Why?

explain

Be a Friend to Trees Read-Aloud

> **Connecting to the Common Core**
> **Reading: Informational Text**
> KEY IDEAS AND DETAILS: K.1

Inferring

Next, show students the cover of the book *Be a Friend to Trees*. Ask

? What do you think this book might be about? Why do you think so?

> **SEP: Obtaining, Evaluating, and Communicating Information**
> Read grade-appropriate texts to obtain scientific information to determine patterns in the natural world.

Determining Importance

Tell students that *Be a Friend to Trees* is a nonfiction book that might help them learn which of the objects came from trees. Introduce the author and

illustrator of the book, and then explain that, as you read, you want them to listen for any of the items they placed in the "From Trees" circle on their sorting charts. Ask them to signal (raise a hand, touch their nose, or in some other way) when they hear about one of the objects.

Questioning

As you read aloud, stop periodically to question students to check for understanding and build interest. Some suggested questions are

? (p. 10) Look at the diagram. What is the first thing that happens in order to make paper? (Wood chips are cooked with chemicals.)

? (p. 10) What are the wood chips called after they become soggy? (pulp)

? (p. 10) What must be done to the pulp after the water is drained off? (It is dried, flattened, and then rolled into paper.)

Explain this process of making paper is a designed system. Engineers and scientists have designed this process and all of the equipment used in the process. There are many parts that work together to make trees into paper.

> **CCC: Systems and System Models**
> Systems in the natural and designed world have parts that work together.

Read on and ask

? (pp. 14–20) What are some of the ways that animals use trees? Turn to a neighbor, and share an example from the book. (Possible answers include the following: Many animals eat leaves, bark, buds, and twigs; squirrels and chipmunks gather nuts to eat; bees collect pollen and nectar; birds roost and nest in trees; and deer hide beneath trees.)

? (p. 21) How do trees help the soil? (They keep it from washing away.)

? (p. 22) What would happen to people and animals if there were no trees or green plants? (There would be no oxygen in the air, and we couldn't breathe.)

Explain that trees are part of a natural system. Parts of the tree provide food and shelter for animals, the roots keep the soil from washing away when it rains, and the leaves provide oxygen for us. Ask

? What happens when we remove trees from this system? (Animals lose their shelter and food, soil washes away, and there is not as much oxygen in the air.)

? (pp. 30–32) What are some things you can do to be a friend to trees? In other words, what can you do to make sure we don't take too many trees out of this natural system? Turn to a neighbor, and share an example from the book. (Answers might include use less paper, reuse paper bags, write on both sides of paper, recycle newspaper, and plant a tree.)

> **CCC: Cause and Effect**
> Events have causes that generate observable patterns.

After reading, give students the opportunity to return to their Sorting Charts and move any of the objects to a different spot on the chart if necessary. Then discuss what kinds of things come from trees (such as oxygen, fruits, nuts, and wood and paper products) and what kinds of things don't (such as carbon dioxide, vegetables, plastics, metals, cloth, glass, and rocks). Ask

? Was there anything you had to move on your sorting chart after reading the book?

? Did anything surprise you?

? How have your ideas changed about what kinds of things come from trees?

elaborate

My Favorite Tree

This activity can be done on school grounds, during a field trip to a park or other wooded area, or as a take-home assignment. Take students outside to look closely at a tree. They will each need a copy of the My Favorite Tree journal, a clipboard, a pencil, and a crayon with the paper removed. First, model how to sketch a tree's shape and make careful observations of its leaves and bark.

Then, show students how to do a leaf rubbing:

1. Find a fallen leaf that is still soft, and place it on your clipboard with the rough or vein side up.
2. Place the journal page over the leaf.
3. Gently rub the long side of the crayon over the leaf.

Next, demonstrate how to do a bark rubbing:

1. Pick the part of the bark that you want to use to make your rubbing.
2. Place the journal page over that part.
3. Gently rub the long side of the crayon over the bark.

Next, model some of your own wonderings about the tree. (For example: How old is this tree? I wonder who planted it. I wonder if an animal lives in this hollow part. What kind of tree is it?)

OBSERVING A LEAF

MAKING A LEAF RUBBING

MAKING A BARK RUBBING

evaluate

We Need Trees Poster

Share your thoughts and feelings about the tree by explaining why you chose the tree as your favorite. (For example: This is my favorite tree because the bark peels up in places and looks like paper. I like how I can fit my arms all the way around the trunk. I have never seen a tree like it before. I feel peaceful when I sit with my back leaning against the trunk.)

Next, model some questions about the tree. (For example: How old is this tree? What type of tree is it? What lives in this tree?)

Then have students complete their journals, which include a drawing of their favorite tree, a leaf rubbing, a bark rubbing, why they like the tree, and questions they have about their tree.

Note: If this activity is to be done at home, students can take their journals home and complete them with an adult helper. If this activity is to be done at school or on a field trip, allow students to look at several trees before deciding on a favorite.

Connecting to the Common Core
Writing
RESEARCH TO BUILD AND PRESENT KNOWLEDGE: K.8

> **SEP: Obtaining, Evaluating, and Communicating Information**
> Communicate information with others in written forms using models, drawings, writing, or numbers that provide detail about scientific ideas.

To summarize the ways people and animals benefit from trees, create a We Need Trees poster. Draw a large picture of a tree trunk with branches on poster paper, and give each student a leaf cutout

copied on green paper. On their leaves, students can write or draw the things trees provide for us and for animals. You may want to revisit the book Be a Friend to Trees to help them as they recall the ways trees are helpful.

Then ask

? What are some good things that trees provide? (shade, paper, homes for squirrels, homes for birds, nuts, apples, syrup, etc.)

Tell students that you would like them to write or draw one good thing we get from trees on each leaf. After students have completed one leaf, they can do more. Fill up the tree poster with as many leaves as possible to show the numerous reasons that we need trees.

Be a Friend to Trees Picture

Next, to demonstrate the ways that we can make choices that will help trees, ask

? What does it mean to "be a friend to trees"? (to do things that will help protect or conserve trees)

? What can we do to be a friend to trees? (Answers may include plant trees, water trees, and recycle paper.)

Have students make pictures of themselves being a friend to trees. Have them label what they are doing in their picture to help trees.

STEM Everywhere

Give students the STEM Everywhere student page as a way to involve their families and extend their learning. They can do the activity with an adult helper and share their results with the class. If students do not have access to internet at home, you may choose to have them complete this activity at school.

Opportunities for Differentiated Instruction

This box lists questions and challenges related to the lesson that students may select to research, investigate, or innovate. Students may also use the questions as examples to help them generate their own questions. These questions can help you move your students from the teacher-directed investigation to engaging in the science and engineering practices in a more student-directed format.

Extra Support

For students who are struggling to meet the lesson objectives, provide a question and guide them in the process of collecting research or helping them design procedures or solutions.

Extensions

For students with high interest or who have already met the lesson objectives, have them choose a question (or pose their own question), conduct their own research, and design their own procedures or solutions.

After selecting one of the questions in this box or formulating their own questions, students can individually or collaboratively make predictions, design investigations or surveys to test their predictions, collect evidence, devise explanations, design solutions, or examine related resources. They can communicate their findings through a science notebook, at a poster session or gallery walk, or by producing a media project.

Continued

Research

Have students brainstorm researchable questions:

? How can trees be identified?

? What is the world's oldest/tallest/thickest tree?

? How is paper made?

Investigate

Have students brainstorm testable questions to be solved through science or math:

? How many different kinds of trees are in the schoolyard?

? What will happen to a leaf on a tree if it is covered with paper for a length of time?

? Can we grow trees from seeds in our classroom?

Innovate

Have students brainstorm problems to be solved through engineering:

? How can we make recycled paper in the classroom?

? In what ways can we use less paper in our classroom?

More Books to Read

Gibbons, G. 1984. *The seasons of Arnold's apple tree.* New York: Voyager Books.
Summary: As the seasons pass, Arnold enjoys a variety of activities as a result of his apple tree. The book includes a recipe for apple pie and a description of how an apple cider press works.

Mora, P. 1994. *Pablo's tree.* New York: Simon & Schuster Books for Young Readers.
Summary: Every year, Pablo's grandfather decorates a special tree for his birthday.

Schaefer, L. M., and A. Schaefer. 2016. *Because of an acorn.* San Francisco: Chronicle Books.
Summary: Die-cut illustrations depict the beautiful chain of events that happen because an acorn grew into an oak tree.

Silverstein, S. 1964. *The giving tree.* New York: Harper & Row.
Summary: In Shel Silverstein's poignant story, a special tree gives a boy many things throughout his life.

Udry, J. 1956. *A tree is nice.* New York: HarperCollins.
Summary: This Caldecott award–winning book speaks simply and elegantly of the many pleasures a tree provides. (Also available in Spanish.)

Worth, B. 2006. *I can name 50 trees today! All about trees.* New York: Random House.
Summary: While stopping to admire some of the world's most amazing trees, the Cat in the Hat and friends teach beginning readers how to identify tree species from the shape of their crowns, leaves, lobes, seeds, bark, and fruit. Dr. Seuss–inspired cartoons and verses teach readers about many of the trees common in North America.

My Favorite Tree

By _____

The Shape of My Favorite Tree

My Favorite Tree cont.

Leaf Rubbing From My Favorite Tree

My Favorite Tree cont.

Bark Rubbing From My Favorite Tree

National Science Teaching Association

My Favorite  Tree cont.

I like this tree because

_____

_____

_____

_____

My questions about this tree are

_____

_____

_____

_____

Leaf Cutout

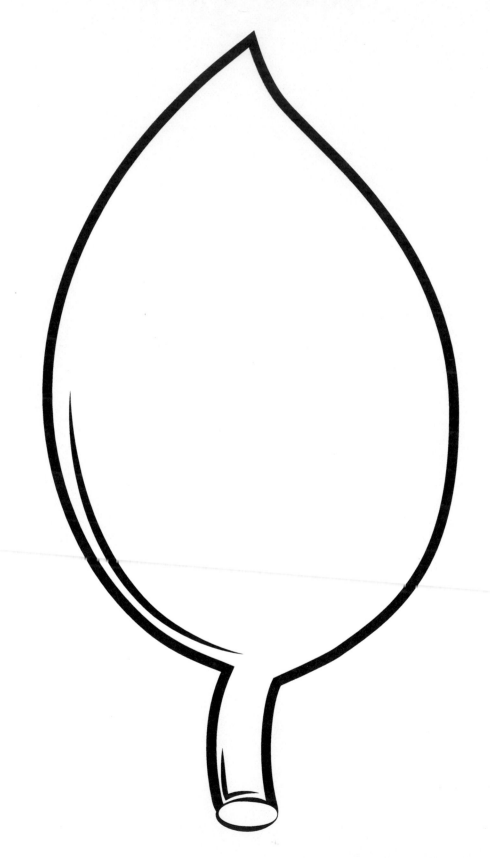

National Science Teaching Association

Name: _____

STEM Everywhere

Dear Families,

At school, we have been learning about **the many ways we benefit from trees** and how we can "be a friend to trees." To find out more, ask your learner the following questions and discuss their answers:

- What did you learn?
- What was your favorite part of the lesson?
- What are you still wondering?

 At home you can watch videos from Sesame Street about trees. To watch the videos, scan the QR code, go to *www.pbslearningmedia.org* and search for "Trees Sesame Street," or go to *www.pbslearningmedia.org/resource/sesame-ken-jeong-deciduous/ken-jeong-deciduous-sesame-street*.

After watching, find a tree in your neighborhood and draw it in the space below. Discuss how this tree helps your neighborhood.